THE YEAR '86
PORTFOOLIO
IN CANADIAN CARICATURE

edited by Guy Badeaux with a text by Charles Gordon

CROC
PUBLISHING

THE AUTHORS

CHARLES GORDON writes a daily humour column for *The Citizen* in Ottawa and a monthly column for *Maclean's* magazine.

GUY BADEAUX is the editorial page cartoonist for *Le Droit* which, convenienty enough, is also published in Ottawa.

THE PUBLISHER

CROC is a humor magazine very famous in Québec that deals irreverently in all matters, delves in parody and is written in a funny language.

This book is the second in a collection that we hope to publish long enough to start worrying about how to incorporate the number 9 in **PORTFOOLIO** before we reach the 90's.

ACKNOWLEDGEMENTS

I would like to thank all the cartoonists involved for making this book possible. I am especially indebted to all those who showed up in Winnipeg this summer for helping in the selection of the drawings. Thanks are also extended to Dale Cummings for organising the whole weekend and to Mike Constable for his hospitality in Toronto.

PLUGS

If you have enjoyed this book, here is a list of some of our contributors' latest publications:

BARRON: *The Best of Barron* / Lester & Orpen Dennys. $9.95

DONATO: *Chins and Needles* / Key Porter Books. $10.95

GIRERD: *M. le Maire de '68 à '86* / Éditions La Presse. $14.95

GORDON: *The Governor General's Bunny Hop* / Macmillan. $17.95

KING: *Tour de Farce* / The Citizen, Ottawa.

KRIEGER: *Bill Bennett: The End* / Douglass & McIntyre. $8.95

NORRIS: *The Best of Norris* / McClelland and Stewart.

PORTFOOLIO 86, THE YEAR IN CANADIAN CARICATURE

National Newspaper Award 1985

Ed Franklin, *The Globe and Mail*, June 22, 1985

FREE TRADE: WOULD YOU BUY
A USED CAR FROM THIS EAGLE?

Nice, quiet little country we've been running here. Full of those cultural and commercial symbols that both enrich and define the land — symbols like Karsh and Masse, Ford and Coca-Cola.

And now they want to change it, make us go out and trade, even-steven, one-on-one with Rambo. As best a student of editorial cartoons can figure it, that's what it means: selling our stuff to Rambo — either him or Cobra or Rocky, all of whom are pretty tough customers, if not known for their intimate and encyclopedic knowledge of fine wines.

Assuming we had any to sell.

There is some confusion, even among cartoonists, as to whether, in trying to sell our fine products, we should be likened to a travelling salesman lured by a lady of the evening, or an innocent virgin about to be taken advantage of by a far too worldly man. Either way, it doesn't look like fun, particularly if Rambo is involved.

Is it sex, is it rape, or just the usual hanky-panky at the drive-in movie? Is it the greatest thing since sliced bread? Is there a tariff on sliced bread? And where do shakes and shingles come in, or go out?

There's another question, about what Rambo and his friends have been doing to our lakes. The answer is they've been doing as much damage to our lakes as we have ourselves, which is pretty fair country damage. Would they have a little chat with us on this topic before we get down to trading? Or should we just say "yes" and get it over with?

The final question is whether Rambo might be soothed a bit by a nice Irish song.

"... Harold, do you have to go on with this Canadian Culture Series... I'm sick and tired of Canadian Culture..!"

. . . were they asking him to sacrifice his culture, his unique Canadian identity, for mere financial rewards in the glittering towers of a foreign publishing company? . . . *I could live with that*, thought Ted!

BEUTEL® TELEGRAPH-JOURNAL

CANADA, AMERICA JUST LIKE 'COUSINS'...REAGAN

EDWARDS
The Whig-Standard

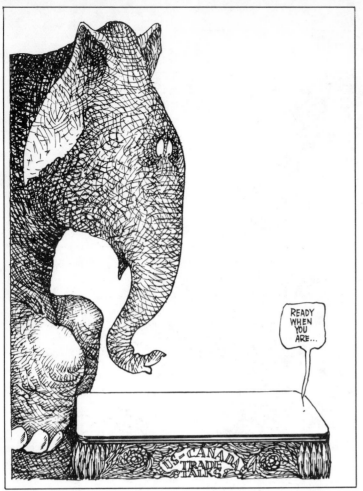

Ed Franklin, *The Globe and Mail*

EN ROUTE POUR LA TABLE DES NÉGOCIATIONS.

Hunter, *Le Soleil*, Québec

Phil Mallette, *The Financial Post*

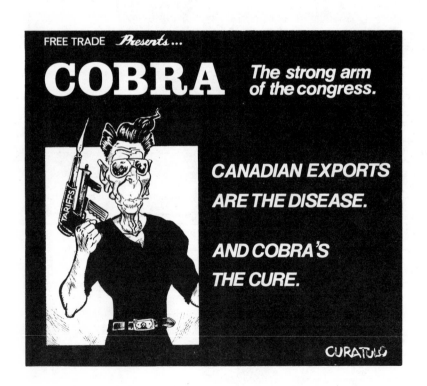

Ed Franklin, *The Globe and Mail*

"Oh dear! . . . Canada and the U.S. have declared free trade talks."

Serge Gaboury, *Le Soleil*, Québec

Anthony Delatri, *Le Nouvelliste*, Trois-Rivières

Bado, *Piranha*

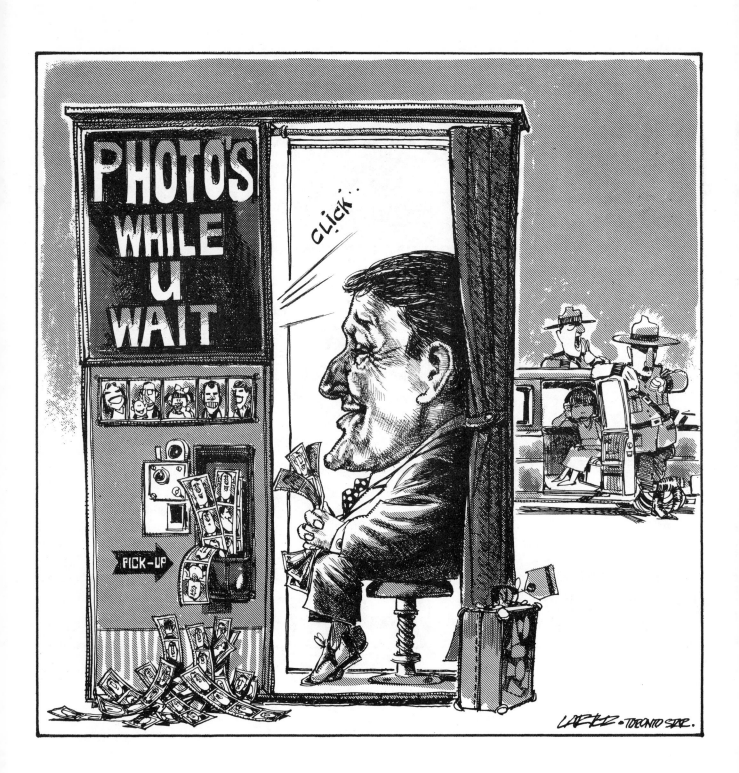

BRIAN, RAMBO. RAMBO, BRIAN.
PLEASED TO MEET YOU.

It wasn't easy. The polls were bad, the budget was unpopular and cabinet ministers kept leaving the room, but our guy, our main man, Brian, was getting ready for his appointment with Rambo. He was doing this by travelling a lot and driving hard bargains. Granted, the hard bargain consisted of getting the most expensive hotel room available, but some people can't even get that.

You think Joe Clark ever got the most expensive hotel room?

Anyway, it's a start. You can never tell when an ability to get the most expensive hotel room might come in handy when you're trying to drive a hard bargain with Rambo or Ronald Reagan or whoever shows up at the table.

It's also useful to practice getting your picture taken, so that you don't look stupid when the chips are down. Our man has been doing that, even to bringing his own videotape crews along in case the media are too cheap to make the trip.

What a guy.

Of course, it would be just like him to blame a media conspiracy for all his problems. Get that. On Sept. 4, 1986, all the cartoonists in Canada, saluted the second anniversary of his election as prime minister. Does that sound like a conspiracy to you? A coincidence, maybe.

Actually, it sounds nice, is what it sounds. And if all the guys in the West drew one cartoon and all the guys in the East drew another, well, that's Canada, isn't it?

Ed Franklin, *The Globe and Mail*

SHAMROCK SUMMIT

Susan Dewar, *The Calgary Sun*

Ed Franklin, *The Globe and Mail*

Roland Pier, le *Journal de Montréal*

Ed Franklin, *The Globe and Mail*

"I got Steven Spielberg to do the special effects."

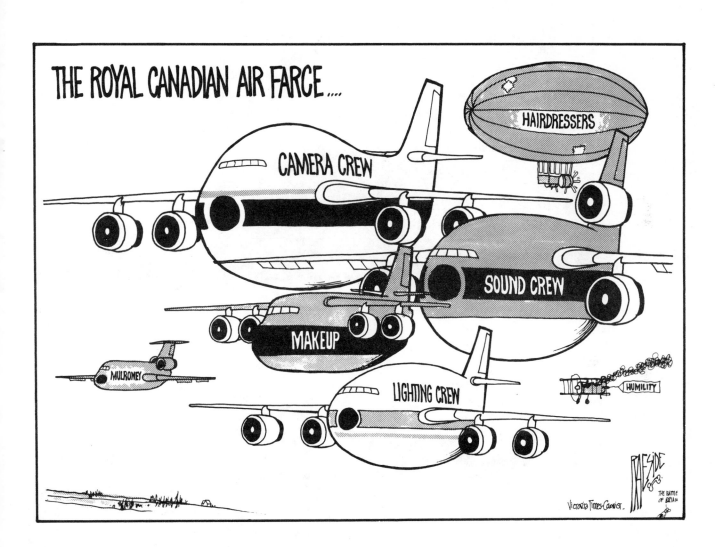

Bado, *Le Droit*, Ottawa

KRIEGER 1986
THE PROVINCE

Anthony Delatri, *Le Nouvelliste,* Trois-Rivières

LA MINE D'OR.

The Gold Mine

GOOD OLD WHAT'SHISNAME,
A GREAT MINISTER OF WHATEVER IT WAS

And how were his colleagues helping Brian get ready to debate Rambo and other silver-tongued American orators?

Well, one guy was tripping over a blind trust. He tried to apologize, saying he didn't realize it was the *trust* that was supposed to be blind.

Another was presenting a budget, thinking that would help.

Another was trying to help young people get jobs and couldn't help it if it looked like she was trying to help the party at the same time.

Another one thought she would help the party if she just went to Europe and tried out limousines for awhile.

Another was throwing burning copies of *Penthouse,* causing a certain amount of discomfort to some of his other colleagues, such as the guy running the taping system and disturbing the cats that still hung around, even though the tuna was long since gone.

Other Canadians tried to help too. And not all of them tripped, slipped, flipped or shipped out. For example, remember Liberals? Remember John Turner? Find a cartoonist who does.

Remember Jean Chretien? Not much of a year for him, except for having a best-selling book and everybody pleading with him to come back and lead the party.

Remember Jacques Hebert — suffering a dearth of food and a glut of publicity. Remember what it was about?

How soon you forget. Remember Sondra Gotlieb? Remember her surprise parties? Remember the surprise? Got a Band-Aid?

CLASS OF '85

Anthony Jenkins, *The Globe and Mail*

TING, *The London Free Press*

What now, Mrs. Blais-Grenier?

Serge Chapleau, *Le Devoir*, Montréal

WILSON CUTS FAMILY ALLOWANCE BAILS OUT BANKS

Canning Season

Moby Dick Part 2

VELCRO LIPS AND SONAR EARS

"Bye dear . . . have a nice day despite being a member of the Tory government."

Bado, *Le Droit*, Ottawa

Jan Kamienski, *The Sun,* Winnipeg

Ed Franklin, *The Globe and Mail*

Mike Constable, *Union Art Services*

Dale Cummings, *The Winnipeg Free Press*

Ed Franklin, *The Globe and Mail*

A BLIND TRUST.

Dale Cummings, *The Winnipeg Free Press*

"Personally, I like Shawn O'Sullivan for the job. He's an excellent puncher and far more diplomatic."

Ed Franklin, *The Globe and Mail*

...IN THIS CORNER, *SONDRA!!*

*MRS. GOTLIEB'S WARDROBE COURTESY OF CANADIAN TIRE.

"Katimavik will relive!"   "At last! Now I can end my hunger strike".   "April fool!"

Roland Pier, le *Journal de Montréal*

Today's youth

LA JEUNESSE D'AUJOURD'HUI...

Bado, *Le Droit*, Ottawa

"It feels better all of a sudden!"

Roland Pier, le *Journal de Montréal*

Dale Cummings, *The Winnipeg Free Press*

Hunter, *Le Soleil*, Québec

...the resumption of normal relations

Phil Mallette, *The Financial Post*

SOMEWHERE IN THE PROVINCES, A GOVERNMENT CHANGED, A DOCTOR CRIED

Remember oil? Remember Alberta? Remember the energy boom?

Remember letting those Eastern bastards freeze in the dark?

Well, maybe saying that was a bit hasty, a bit harsh. We all make mistakes. Even Alberta makes mistakes. No hard feelings, eh?

Eh?

EH!?! Somebody answer, please!

Apparently – heh, heh – it's possible for people other than Easterners to freeze. Even British Columbians – although nobody there ever freezes unless they are silly enough not to have a roof over their heads. Only people silly enough to get in the way of Expo '86 were in that category.

There was an inclination to blame that on the government of the day, but it appears that the leader of the government of that day wandered off into the Pacific sunset, leaving behind him a fine fair, a slightly larger homeless population and a successor much beloved of cartoonists, although feared by flies.

There were no flies on Quebec. Just a new government, that appeared strangely like an old government. In Ontario, the new government appeared strangely like a new government. Shocked and alarmed at this development, traditionalists called for the doctor. And called, and called...

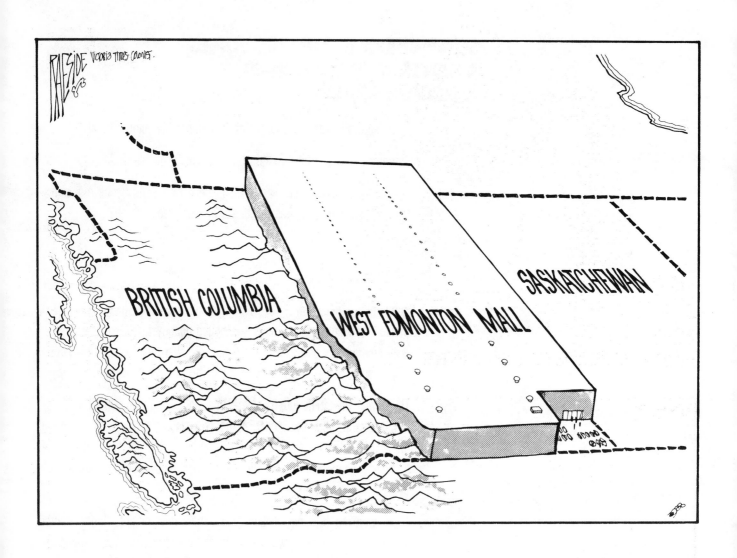

"... foreclosures, grasshoppers, drought, floods, grain prices... just when I thought things couldn't possibly get worse, I strike oil!"

GAINERS SAUSAGE
INGREDIENTS: PORK
WATER
BREAD-CRUMBS
SCABS

Mike Constable, *Union Art Services*

EXPO 86
SOUVENIR DOLLS

Mike Constable, *Union Art Services*

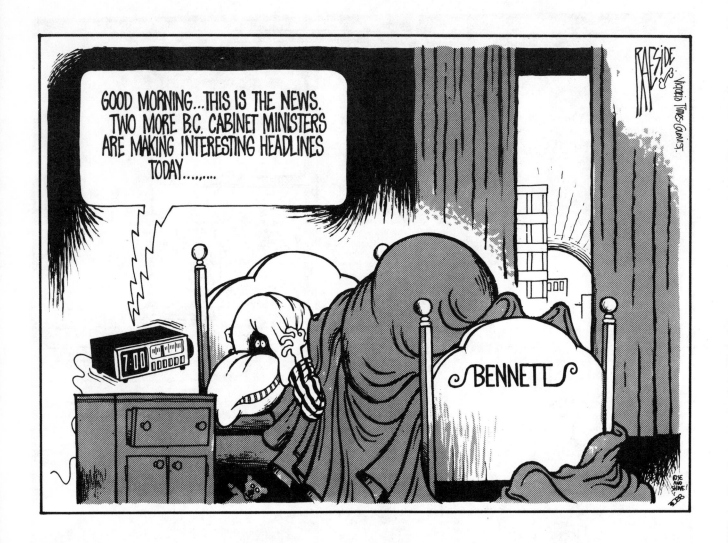

Bado, *Le Droit*, Ottawa

IF YOU HAD A CHOICE, WHO WOULD YOU PREFER TO BE THE NEW PREMIER?....

IF YOU HAD A CHOICE, WOULD YOU PREFER TO BE RUN OVER BY A TRAIN, A TRUCK OR A HERD OF STAMPEDING ELEPHANTS?....

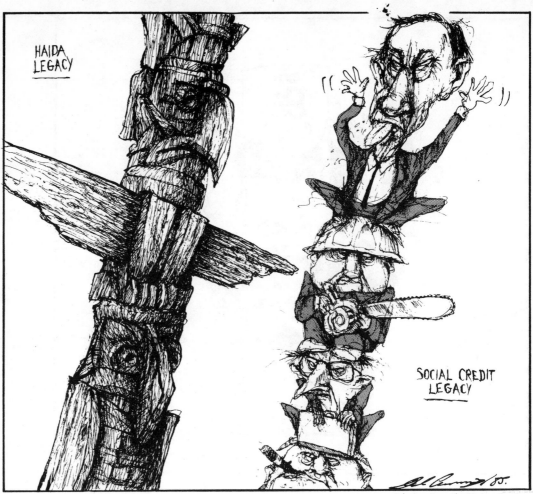

HAIDA
LEGACY

SOCIAL CREDIT
LEGACY

Dale Cummings, *The Winnipeg Free Press*

PASSING
THE
TORCH

MURPHY
THE PROVINCE
VANCOUVER

Bado, *Le Droit,* Ottawa

Girerd, *La Presse*, Montréal

"I am very happy for the Liberals."

Roland Pier, le *Journal de Montréal*

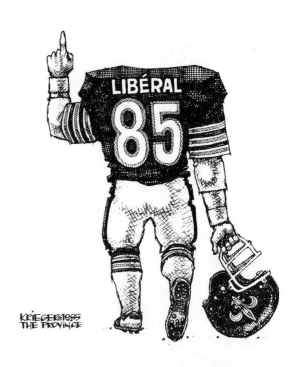

LE
SUMMIT

JF TODD '86©

First budget: Bourassa has kept his promises

PREMIER BUDGET

BOURASSA
A TENU
SES PROMESSES

Serge Chapleau, *Le Devoir*, Montréal

L'ENRACINEMENT DU PARTI CONSERVATEUR

The Conservatives taking root

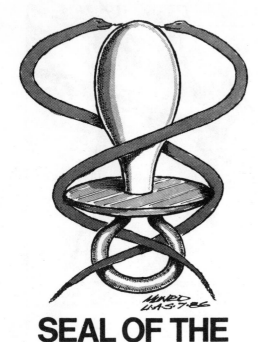

SEAL OF THE ONTARIO MEDICAL ASSOCIATION

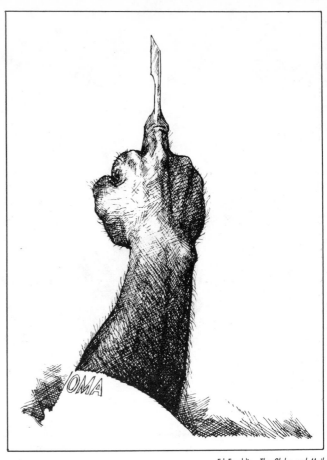

Ed Franklin, *The Globe and Mail*

19th Century Ontario doctors applied leeches to their patients

20th Century Ontario doctors apply extra billing.

Both are blood suckers

Mike Constable, *Union Art Services*

"That's my wallet!"

"... no, no, Harold... I don't mean that at all... it's a wonderful, unique decorating idea... it just makes me sick to my stomach sometimes, that's all..."

A GALLERY OF MISCELLANY:
REMEMBER CIGARETTES?
REMEMBER MONEY?

The dollar was so bad that the Queen wanted off the bill. You could look it up.

A new dollar coin was coming and you can guess how truly excited the population was about that.

Although it is possible that they didn't run to the bank to snap up the new money because the bank wasn't there.

In truth, the entire monetary situation might have driven you to drink, but you had to be careful what. There were secret ingredients in the wine.

Cigarettes weren't much fun either. Neither were airplanes, particularly if they were full of Tories and even if they weren't.

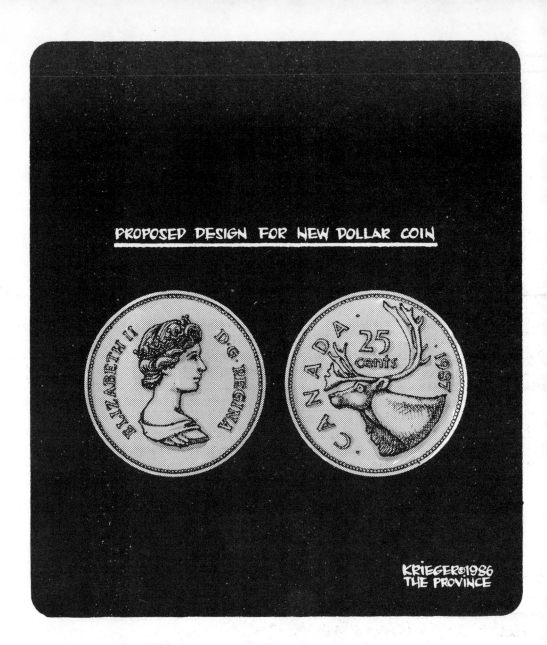

PROPOSED DESIGN FOR NEW DOLLAR COIN

KRIEGER©1986
THE PROVINCE

Susan Dewar, *The Calgary Sun*

NEW ISSUE

DONATO
TORONTO SUN

Ed Franklin, *The Globe and Mail*

"So? How much can you lend us?"

© 1985 MAYE

OPENING SOON
ANOTHER ALBERTA
BASED BANK

RAESIDE

Q: WHICH WESTERN BANK
GETS NO GOVT. BAILOUTS,
GUARANTEES ALL DEPOSITS,
AND HAS <u>NEVER</u> MADE A BAD LOAN?....

A:

FOOD BANK

REGULATION

DeRegulation

Bado, *Le Droit*, Ottawa

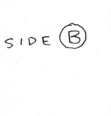

SIDE Ⓐ

FOLD TABS AFTER USE

AIR
SICKNESS
BAG

SIDE Ⓑ

NO
POSTAGE
REQUIRED

HON. DON MAZANKOWSKI
PARLIAMENT BLD
OTTAWA

AIR CANADA PASSENGERS CONTINUE TO VOICE THEIR OPINION OF TORY GOVT.

Mike Constable, Union Art Services

"...SHOULD CABIN PRESSURE FALL, OXYGEN IS AVAILABLE... BY THE WAY, DID I MENTION HOW MUCH I ADMIRE AND RESPECT THE CONSERVATIVE PARTY?..."

THE OFFICIAL TORY STEWARDESS...

AIR BRIAN

MULDOON HEADGEAR AND WALKMAN!

MICHAEL WILSON SEQUINED, PICK-YOUR-POCKET, PIGSKIN GLOVE.

S.S.S. (SAVE SINC STEVENS) ARMBAND.

PC LOGO KERCHIEF.

COLOGNE 'EAU DE THON' (TUNA WATER).

DON'T KISS ME I'M IRISH

AUTHORIZED PASSENGER READING MATERIAL. ① LATEST HACK BIOGRAPHY OF MULRONEY ② THE P.C. CANADA FUND MONTHLY BULLETIN (FEATURED THIS ISSUE: EXCERPTS FROM LATEST HACK BIOGRAPHY ETC.). ③ NEW, IN-AIR MAGAZINE, "EN SWILL," EDITED BY JOURNALIST (WHO WROTE LATEST HACK BIO ETC.).

ERIK NIELSEN PUNK BRACELET.

OFFICIAL P.C. FUND RAISER BUTTON, "WITH YOUR HELP, WE CAN PUT A CABINET MINISTER THROUGH HIGH SCHOOL!!"

"SENSIBLE TOGS" BY FLORA N' CARNEY.

TORY POOP + SCOOP.

"FREE QUÉBEC TORIES" ANKLET.

FEET OF BAIE COMEAU CLAY.

AISLIN 86
MONTREAL GAZETTE

The military's worst nightmare...

American Gothic 1985

Serge Gaboury, *Le Soleil*, Québec

Jan Kamienski, *The Sun*, Winnipeg

" I'M YOUR ANTI-FREEZE STEWARD, SIR, MAY I SUGGEST
A GUTSY AUSTRIAN OR ITALIAN IMPORT ? "

TING, *The London Free Press*

Dale Cummings, *The Winnipeg Free Press*

"Be with you in a while . . . right after today's Thank-You-for-Coming-to-Work Awards ceremony."

Ed Franklin, *The Globe and Mail*

Dale Cummings, *The Winnipeg Free Press*

YOU COULD BE RAMBO'S FRIEND TOO, IF YOU PLAYED YOUR CARDS RIGHT

We figured we were having trouble with Rambo! And our guy is Rambo's friend.

There are countries where Rambo has few friends. Many countries like that. Imagine living in a country where Rambo has no friends.

What Rambo does, if he finds a country with no friends, is he finds some friends and talks them into going into that country. That way, Rambo will have some friends there. It is a pretty clever idea when you think about it. A place like Nicaragua is an example of that.

Nicaragua must be one of those places that does not need tourist dollars all that bad, because it is not inviting in Rambo's friends for dinner. Some say this has little to do with Rambo's friends and everything to do with there not being any dinner for them.

Rambo's friends wind up hanging around places like Honduras which they say are not as nice as Nicaragua used to be. Apparently there is no Statue of Liberty in Nicaragua, and no Welcome Wagon either.

As for some of the other countries that Rambo is not friends with, he is testing bombs and thinking about it.

REAGAN AND
THE SANDINISTA—
LIBYAN THREAT

"See any light at the end of the tunnel?"

I'M AFRAID YOU WERE RIGHT, MAD DOG KHADAFY DOES HAVE RABIES...
GRRRRRRRRRR..
A
TOL
BCOD
RTSL
MRTL
EOBKL
LARTER
TORONTO STAR!
WAR

WHO KNOWS ABOUT SOUTH AFRICA?

The great thing about South Africa is that everybody knows how to fix it right up.

The (white) South Africans know; the Americans know; the British know. The cartoonists know. Even Brian knows.

The difficulty is that what one guy knows is not necessarily what the next guy does. There is a problem about what the British know. According to the cartoonists, who should know, what Thatcher knows is not exactly the same as what Queen Elizabeth knows.

Then there is the question about what the black South Africans know. The white South Africans are making it more and more difficult to know this.

The hungry know, the imprisoned know, the oppressed know. Mandela knows. Tutu knows.

With everybody knowing, you'd think someone could figure out how to avoid bloodshed. Do you know?

Dale Cummings, *The Winnipeg Free Press*

THE ETIQUETTE OF APARTHEID...

Mike Constable, *Union Art Services*

SOUTH AFRICAN SCHOOLS CLOSED. PHYS-ED CONTINUES

Mike Constable, *Union Art Services*

Too late for a handshake in South Africa

IL EST TROP TARD POUR SE SERRER LA MAIN EN AFRIQUE DU SUD

Girerd, *La Presse*, Montréal

South Africa

"If they want to be equal, we must raise them to our level, don't we?"

Girerd, *La Presse*, Montréal

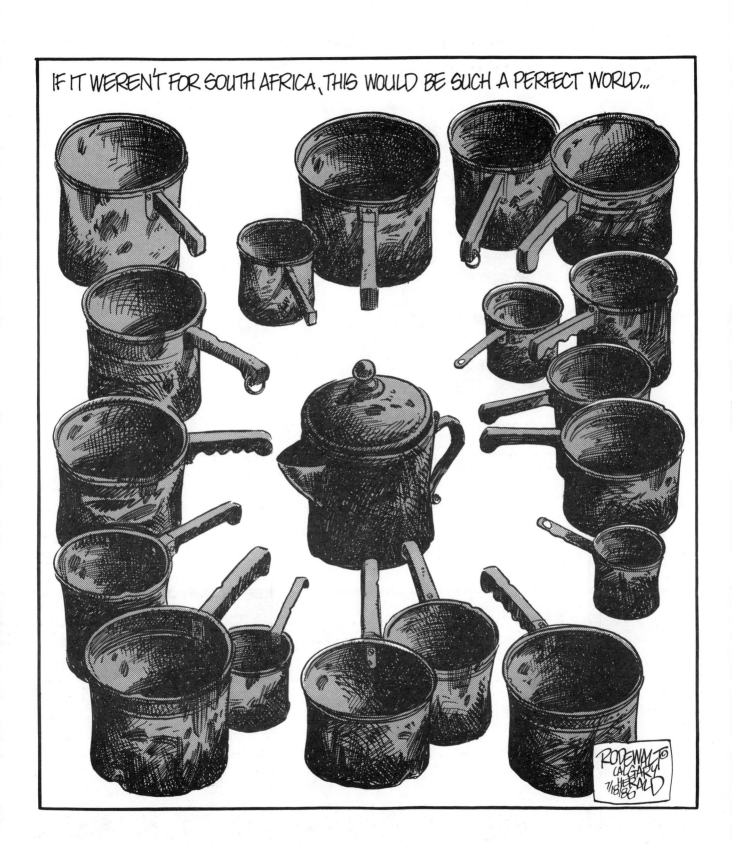

IF IT WEREN'T FOR SOUTH AFRICA, THIS WOULD BE SUCH A PERFECT WORLD...

BLACK OUT
EN AFRIQUE DU SUD!

Serge Chapleau, *Le Devoir*, Montréal

Editorial

In South Africa THIS is a subversive, anti-government misuse of FREE SPEECH... on the other hand, this is WHITE space.

BEUTEL® TELEGRAPH-JOURNAL

"What worries me is what those economic sanctions are going to do to our lifestyle!"

NO SANCTIONS

U.K. RULES!

mallette

WINNIPEG FREE PRESS

Phil Mallette, *The Winnipeg Free Press*

"I think I remember losing to his guy in the '84 Olympics, or was it the '80 Olympics?... '72?... '36?..."

Dale Cummings, *The Winnipeg Free Press*

MARGARET...ABOUT OUR LITTLE QUARREL OVER SANCTIONS...I'VE CONSULTED MY
ADVISERS AS TO THE TRADITIONAL BRITISH METHOD FOR RESOLVING DISPUTES
WITH THE CROWN...

Dale Cummings, *The Winnipeg Free Press*

RAMBO MEETS KHADAFY. DUCK!

It's not that everyone was making it all that easy for Rambo. Terrorists, kidnappers, bombers – the more they did, the more frustrated Rambo became, until...

But that's getting ahead of the story – which is that the more they did, the more they bombed, kidnapped and terrorized, the more sympathy Rambo got.

He thought to himself: "What would Rambo do?" Then he did it. This was tough on the tourist trade, tough on just about everybody. But that's what happens when you mess with Rambo.

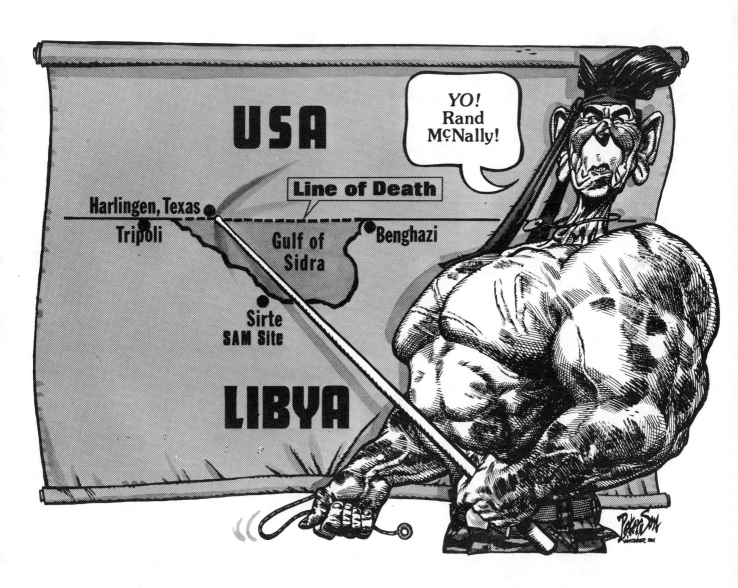

Girerd, *La Presse*, Montréal

Allah holds him in his arms...

Serge Chapleau, *Le Devoir*, Montréal

"Thought it'd speed things up thru security"

Dale Cummings, *The Winnipeg Free Press*

WHERE HAVE ALL THE SLAYERS GONE?

The world could hardly stand all the bad stuff that was going on. Cartoonists could barely keep up with it.

What made it particularly tough to take was the departure of fun-loving old friends. True, Kurt Waldheim was going to be around for a while, but Duvalier – you thought Duvalier would always be around, but he was gone. And Marcos – not only did Ferdie Marcos split, but his wife took all the shoes.

Plus there was no guarantee that the new bunch would be any fun at all. Certainly, if you liked shoes you were in for a let-down.

WALDHEIM

"They now have proof that Waldheim is Hitler without a moustache."

NOW THE ELECTION IS OVER, IT'S TIME TO RECONSTRUCT AND REBUILD...

VOTE KURT

....STARTING WITH A BIGGER CLOSET.

WAR RECORD

Ed Franklin, *The Globe and Mail*

LE PRÉSIDENT MARCOS

ILYA DES ACCIDENTS DE TRAINS ET D'AVIONS ··· ILYA LE CANCER ET LE SIDA ··· ILYA DUVALIER ET MARCOS

Girerd, *La Presse*, Montréal

Dale Cummings, *The Winnipeg Free Press*

Bado, *Le Droit*, Ottawa

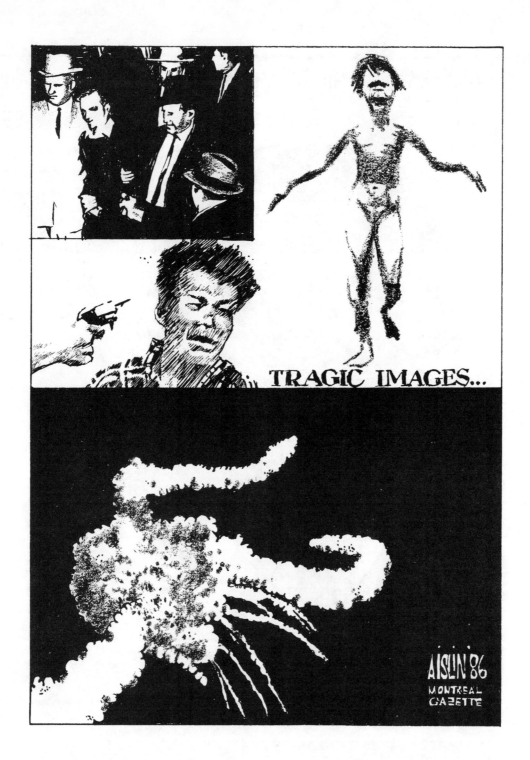

THE WONDERFUL WORLD OF TECHNOLOGY

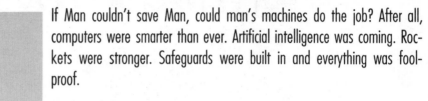

If Man couldn't save Man, could man's machines do the job? After all, computers were smarter than ever. Artificial intelligence was coming. Rockets were stronger. Safeguards were built in and everything was foolproof.

At Chernobyl, as in Kansas City, everything was up to date. Wasn't it?

"Here is a small news item from Kiev!"

DEWAR '86 CALGARY SUN

MAY DAY 1986

DONATO
TORONTO SUN

HOW THE CRUISE MISSILE IS CAPABLE OF WIPING OUT THE RUSSIANS...

A CRUISE RELEASED. MOTOR KICKS IN.

B GUIDANCE SYSTEM TAKES OVER.

C CRUISE IMPACTS.

D RUSSIANS DIE LAUGHING.

WHERE CONTENTED CATTLE GRAZE...

MOO

U.S. CRUISE

Dale Cummings, *The Winnipeg Free Press*

"Isn't this something, Harry, the great outdoors... it's so quiet, you could hear a..."

Jan Kamienski, *The Sun*, Winnipeg

MUST YOU GO DOWN TO THE SEA IN SHIPS?

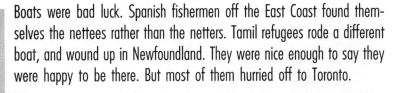

Boats were bad luck. Spanish fishermen off the East Coast found them-selves the nettees rather than the netters. Tamil refugees rode a different boat, and wound up in Newfoundland. They were nice enough to say they were happy to be there. But most of them hurried off to Toronto.

Don't forget, though you may want to, the Polar Sea, the Rainbow Warrior, the Achille Lauro. It wasn't a great year for sailing over the bounding main, whatever the bounding main is.

Dale Cummings, *The Winnipeg Free Press*

C'est la Guerre

IMAGINE...

THOUGHTS FOR FOOD

On Nov. 28, 1985, all the cartoonists in North America, give or take a few, drew cartoons, comic strips, wall hangings, graffiti, whatever, in honor, if that can be the word, of world hunger.

Nov. 28 was American Thanksgiving, a funny day for Canadian cartoonists to be doing their thing for world hunger, but that's the way things happen on this continent. The cartoonists may have been ahead of the politicians — free trade in cartoons.

Mary Worth, it is our sad duty to point out, forgot all about world hunger. But the folks between these covers didn't.

The other side of Third World Hunger is First World Affluence. Hunger isn't funny, but affluence is, when it's not being obscene. And sometimes obscenity is funny too.

Cartoonists won't solve world hunger, but nobody else is doing much of a job either. Certainly, not the politicians. And we're not getting all that many laughs out of them either.

THE OUTCASTS

IT SAYS HERE THAT MORE ROCK STARS ARE THINKING OF VISITING ETHIOPIA

YOU'D HAVE THOUGHT THEY'D SUFFERED ENOUGH

11/28/85   © TSS Frick

FURTREE HIGH

A meeting for all the students was held today in the cafeteria.

A donation for famine relief was to be sent to a country chosen by the pupils.

Half the cafeteria felt that hunger-stricken Ethiopia should get the donation, while the other half opted for the starving Sudan. Tempers flared.

The resulting food fight took four hours to bring under control.

THE THIRD WORLD

WILL THE REAL SPIRIT OF CHRISTMAS
PLEASE STAND UP...

Bado, *Le Droit,* Ottawa

Born in 1966, **Cuyler Black** was just 17 years old when his daily comic strip *Furtree High* debuted in the Ottawa *Citizen* in January 1984. On the fringe of being 20 now, he and the strip are still going strong, as he tackles the demands of Queen's University in Kingston. Rejected by every major syndicate in the known world, he still pursues that elusive goal in order that he may quit his other part-time job as a speed bump in a Kingston parking lot.

BIOGRAPHIES

Aislin is the name of **Terry Mosher**'s eldest daughter and the *nom de plume* he uses as the editorial page cartoonist for *the Gazette* in Montréal. Syndicated by *The Toronto Star,* he has freelanced in the U.S. and abroad for such publications as *The New York Times, Time Magazine, The National Lampoon, Harper's, The Atlantic Monthly* and *Punch Magazine.* Born in Ottawa in 1941, he is a graduate of Quebec City's École des Beaux-Arts. Aislin has won a number of citations including two Canadian National Newspaper Awards (1977 and 1978), the prestigious Quill Award... "for outstanding contributions to the flow of public information on Canadian affairs," and five individual prizes from The International Salon of Cartoons and Caricatures. In May of 1985, Aislin was the youngest person ever to be inducted into The Canadian News Hall of Fame.

Bado is **Guy Badeaux**'s last name pronounced phonetically. Born in Montréal in 1949, he has worked there, left and right, for a wide spectrum of publications *(The Montreal Star, The Gazette, The Financial Times, Le Devoir, Le Jour, Mainmise, Baloune, Le Temps Fou, Montreal Review, Le 30...)* half of which have since either folded or moved to Toronto. He moved to Ottawa in 1981 to become the editorial-page cartoonist of *Le Droit.* This year he was named president of the Association of Canadian Cartoonists mostly because he was bilingual.

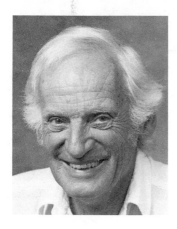

Born in Toronto in 1917, **Sid Barron** moved to Victoria with his family as a very young child. In 1959 he took a crack at drawing editorial page cartoons for *The Victoria Times* and two years later joined *The Toronto Star* where he was hired on by Pierre Berton. Barron has had an on-and-off working relationship with the paper ever since.

Josh Beutel was born and educated in Montréal, Québec. He majored in drawing and painting, graduating from Sir George Williams University (now Concordia U.) in 1966. Following graduation, he taught art in high schools in Ontario and Labrador while freelancing political cartoons for various newspapers. Cartoonist for the Saint-John *Telegraph-Journal* and *Evening Times-Globe,* since the fall of 1978, his work is syndicated in the United States and Europe by Rothco Cartoons Inc. His cartoons have been published in *Newsweek, The Financial Post, New York Times, Chicago Tribune, World Press Review,* and *London Observer.*

"... look, Harold... packages of transparent Forbidden signs you can put up anywhere on anything to stop people doing things..."

Born in Amsterdam in 1921, **Bob Bierman** did some work for various Dutch publications after the war before emigrating to Canada in 1950. First working as a bar doorman in Toronto, he soon moved west to BC. In 1954, he published his first cartoon in *The Victoria Times*. In June of 1978 he drew a cartoon of then Human Resources Minister Bill Vander Zalm pulling wings off flies, which was printed by the *Times*. Vander Zalm successfully sued the *Times* and Bierman for libel but the decision was overturned by the Supreme Court. He has, since 1976, been working on a regular basis for *Monday* in Victoria and recently started his own syndication.

Blaine was born in Glace Bay, Nova Scotia. He has been the editorial page cartoonist of the Hamilton *Spectator* since 1961. Winner of the National Newspaper Award in 1974 and again in 1982, he is the only Canadian cartoonist to win the coveted Reuben Award in New York (1970). First winner of the Grand Prize at Montreal's International Salon of Cartoons in 1965, Blaine has also freelanced for *The New York Times, Time* and *Playboy*. A black-belt instructor in karate, he also writes music and sings.

Born in Ottawa in 1960, **Cameron Cardow** (Cam) attented Sheridan College in 1983, where he studied illustration. In 1984, he joined *The Citizen* in Ottawa as a staff artist and a year later was asked to submit one cartoon a week on a free-lance basis.

Born in Montréal in 1945 and having studied painting and graphic arts at l'École des Beaux-Arts, **Serge Chapleau** became an instant celebrity in Québec in 1972 with a weekly full-colour caricature for *Perspectives*. He joined *Montréal-Matin* two years later where he did editorial cartoons until the paper folded following a long strike. He regained stardom (or at least his voice did) when a puppet character of his, Gérard D. Laflaque (seen in the photo), became a suppertime regular on public TV. Despite huge ratings, the one-minute-and-fifteen-second daily program was deemed too sarcastic and was canceled after its first year. Serge has recently resurfaced at the very sedate *Le Devoir* where he does three cartoons a week. Gérard D. can now be seen on a private network.

Mike Constable was born in Woodstock, Ontario in 1943. After studying sculpture at the Ontario College of Art, he moved on to Carlton University in Ottawa where he studied sociology. He was a co-founder of *Gorilla,* a Toronto underground newspaper from 1969 through 1974. In 1977 he was one of the founders of Union Art Services, a co-operative mailing service of graphics and cartoons, which presently goes out to about forty-five labour publications. Besides freelancing for *Saturday Night, TO Magazine, Canadian Tribune,* The Globe & Mail's *Report on Business,* he is editor of *Piranha* (Toronto's National Humour Magazine) and has recently started a gag cartoon panel (*Left Lobe*) in *The Toronto Star.*

Born in 1948 in St. Thomas, Ontario, **Dale Cummings** studied animation and illustration at Sheridan College in Oakville. In 1974, he became one of the chief animators in the production of *True North,* the first successful attempt to include animated caricatures in a documentary film on Canadian politics and life. During a brief stay in New York he did some cartoons for *The New York Times.* He returned to Toronto in 1976, where he freelanced for *The Last Post, The Canadian Forum, Maclean's, The Toronto Star, Canadian Magazine* and *This Magazine.* Full-time editorial cartoonist with *The Winnipeg Free Press* since 1981, he won the National Newspaper Award in 1983.

REAGAN SLAPS WRISTS
BOTHA DOESN'T

MC

Born the second last day of 1958, **Fred Curatolo** was encouraged by Andy Donato in 1980 to take a shot at editorial cartooning. Two years later, he got his first cartoon published with the Toronto *Sun* and has, since then, been filling in on holidays and days off for Donato.

Anthony Delatri was born in Pennsylvania in 1922 and grew up in rural Québec, but returned to the US at the age of seventeen to join the Army and served overseas during the Second World War. He studied later at the Newark School of Fine and Industrial Art, while drawing for several American publications. During this period, he also tried out as a pitcher for the New York Giants. By the 1950s, he was back in Québec. He did occasional drawings for *Le Journal de Montréal, Montréal-Matin,* and *Dimanche Matin* until becoming the full-time editorial cartoonist for *Le Nouvelliste* in Trois-Rivières in 1967.

Born in Montréal in 1949, **Susan Dewar** attended high school in Toronto, went to Western University, in London, and graduated from Toronto Teacher's College. In 1972 she travelled all over Europe and worked in Germany for two years as tour guide. Back in Canada, she taught Cree children on native reserve and elementary grades in Toronto for two years. After working in commercial art and cartooning in Toronto, she started her company (Dewar's Ink) freelancing for *Canadian Forum, Bridges, Teen Generation Current* and the Toronto *Sun*. She joined *The Calgary Sun* as full-time editorial cartoonist in 1984.

Andy Donato was born in Scarborough in 1937. He graduated from Danforth Technical School in 1955 and began working at Eaton's as a layout artist. He left Eaton's in 1959 to join a small art studio and after a year decided to freelance. He joined the Toronto *Telegram* in 1961 as a graphic artist working in the promotion department. In 1963 he worked on the redesign of the paper and joined the editorial department. In 1968 he was appointed art director and began cartooning on a part-time basis. After the demise of the *Telegram* he joined the Toronto *Sun* as art director and produced two cartoons a week. In 1974, Donato took over cartooning on a fulltime basis. In 1985-86, he served as the second Canadian-born president of the Association of American Editorial Cartoonists.

Frank A. Edwards was born in Belleville, Ontario in 1940. After graduating from the Ontario College of Art, he worked as a commercial artist for several printing companies. In 1965, Frank accepted a position with Queen's University where he worked for 13 years as a medical illustrator. In 1978, he joined *The Whig Standard* in Kingston as its first full-time cartoonist. His work is syndicated in Canada and the United States.

Born in 1958, and after attending art school for two years, **Dave Elston** began freelancing full-time at the age of 21. One of his first breaks was doing a weekly sports cartoon for *The Calgary Sun*. He recently started his own sports cartoon syndicate, and in April of 1985 began filling in for Susan Dewar on the *Sun's* editorial page.

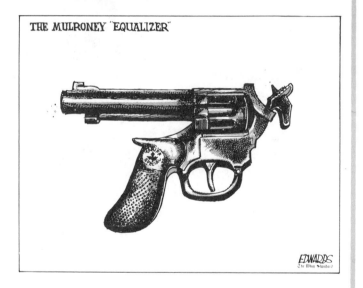

Born in Texas in 1921, **Ed Franklin** started his career at *The Houston Press* in 1947 and, several years later, moved over to *The Houston Post*. In 1952, he went to New York to study at the Pratt Institute. In the fall of 1959, he visited Toronto and, feeling it would be a good place to bring up his kids, has been there ever since. First freelancing for *The Globe and Mail,* he then moved over to *The Toronto Star* for a while, filling in for Duncan Macpherson. In 1968, he moved back to the *Globe* alternating on the editorial page with Jim Reidford and became the daily cartoonist when Reidford retired in 1972. Developing his own style as a fine caricaturist, he does away with signing his drawings which didn't prevent him from winning the National Newspaper Award in 1985.

Born in 1949 in Saskatoon, **Brian Gable** studied fine arts at the University of Saskatchewan. Graduating with a B.Ed. from the University of Toronto in 1971, he taught art in Brockville and began freelancing for *The Brockville Recorder and Times* in 1977. In 1980 he started full-time with *The Regina Leader Post.*

Born in Quebec City in 1954, **Serge Gaboury** started publishing cartoons at the age of 20. He has been drawing comic strips in *Croc* since 1979. Two collections of his work have since been published there: *La vie c'est mourant* and *Gaboury croque encore*. Besides working in animated films, he publishes sports cartoons in *Le Soleil* and does the editorial page drawing during Hunter's holidays. He has won two prizes at the Montréal International Salon of Cartoons (1981 and 1982).

Born in Sault Ste. Marie in 1934, **Dick Gibson** has been working for the past 10 years at the toronto *Sun* where both his political and situation cartoons have been featured. Right now his work appears across Canada and in some papers in the United States through Canada-Wide Feature Services. He has also been doing a drawing every week in the Bampton *Guardian* under the name of **Teasdale.**

Jean-Pierre Girerd was born in 1931 in Algeria, where he studied art at l'École Nationale des Beaux-Arts for five years. In 1956 he was hired as a political cartoonist for the *Journal d'Alger*. In 1961 being a *pied noir* in Algeria was not very comfortable, so Girerd decided to move to the U.S., where he worked for *The Minneapolis Star* as a cartoonist and illustrator. Deciding that America was not for him, he settled in Paris. He came to Montréal on a holiday in 1964, and decided that he wouldn't mind living there, working in his native language. He worked for the newspaper *Métro Express* until it folded. After Berthio left *La Presse,* Girerd was hired as their editorial-page cartoonist and has been working there ever since. In 1985 he was named to the Order of Canada and won the Grand Prize at the Montréal International Salon of Cartoons.

Mike Graston was born in Montréal in 1954. After graduating with an honors history degree from the University of Western Ontario, he was hired in a freelance capacity by the Ottawa *Citizen* in 1977. In January 1980, he moved to a full-time editorial cartooning position with *The Windsor Star.*

Raoul Hunter was born in Saint-Cyrille de l'Islet, Québec in 1926. After attending l'École des Beaux-Arts in Quebec City, he studied art history in Paris on a scholarship. Returning to Québec, he began to make a name for himself as a sculptor while teaching at l'École des Beaux-Arts. In 1956 he became the editorial cartoonist of *Le Soleil*. Finding three careers rather hectic, he gave up teaching in 1969. Hunter draws eight cartoons a week for *Le Soleil* and its regional editions and has won the National Newspaper Award in 1958 and 1967.

Tom Innes was born in Salem, Oregon in 1923. His family migrated to Canada five years later and settled in the Calgary area. During the 1930's, his family moved to Vancouver, where he lived until the war broke out. In 1942 he joined the Navy and, after the war, enrolled at the Calgary School of Technology and Art. He packed it in after two years and, after working in numerous jobs, became, in 1956, a paste-up artist. He soon joined the staff of *The Calgary Herald* as editorial-page cartoonist and has been with the paper ever since. He won the National Newspaper Award in 1981.

LA GROSSE MACHINE BLEUE.

"A little something I picked up in Ottawa!"

Born in Toronto in 1951, **Anthony Jenkins** graduated in Arts from the University of Waterloo. His work has appeared in *The Globe and Mail* since 1974. He has backpacked through 57 countries in Europe, Asia, Africa and South America. The results, in prose and penwork, has recently been published as *Traveller's Tales — An Illustrated Journey*. He has spent the last year travelling the Americas from Alaska to Terra del Fuego.

Born in Poland in 1923, **Jan Kamienski** studied art in Paris and Dresden and worked full-time in film animation. He came to Canada in 1949, and worked as commercial artist until 1958, when he joined the now-defunct Winnipeg *Tribune* until its closure in 1980. Since November 1980, he is staff cartoonist for The Winnipeg *Sun*. Over the years, he has won many awards including: City of Dresden Award for Graphic Work (1946), Art Directors Club of Toronto Award for Best Institutional Page (1957), Award of the Salon International de Caricature (1963), and National Newspaper Award for Editorial Cartooning (1964).

MAKE A WISH

NEWS ITEM: GULF MAY TAKE OVER HIRAM WALKER.

Jim Kempkes was born in Buffalo, New York, in 1947 and came to Canada in 1969. He studied fine arts at York University in Toronto where he was especially influenced by the drawing and sculpture of Honoré Daumier. Since then he has worked freelance, specializing in sculptural caricature in addition to contributing drawings to the Union Art Service and other publications.

Born in Belfast, Northern Ireland, in 1947, **Alan King** came to Canada with his family at the age of two. After graduating in English Literature from University of Western Ontario he taught high-school English, and worked as a piano salesman, a taxi driver, an engineering technician, an illustrator and an ad agency art director. Having studied classical music as a child and at the university level, he still plays as much piano as he has time for. Married, with one son, he has been with *The Citizen,* in Ottawa, since 1979 and is now doing five cartoons a week.

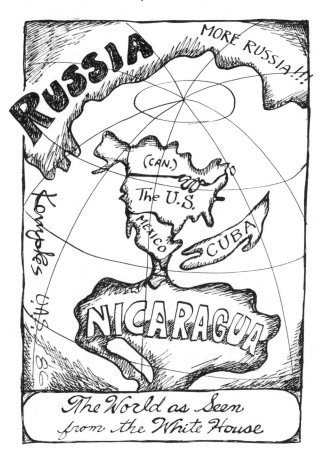

Born in Vancouver in 1954, **Bob Krieger** has been drawing political cartoons for *The Province* since 1981 where he now shares duties with illegal alien Dan Murphy. Krieger's work has also appeared in *Iaccoca, The Last Days of MASH, School Wars, The Expo Story* and *Bill Bennett: The End.*

Born in Swift Current, Saskatchewan in 1950, **John Larter** started at *The Lethbridge Herald* in 1974, went to *The Edmonton Sun* in 1978 and then to *The Toronto Star* in 1980.

Probably the most celebrated cartoonist in Canada, **Duncan Macpherson** was born in Toronto in 1924. Associated with *The Toronto Star's* editorial page since 1958, Macpherson has won the National Newspaper Award an unprecedented six times in 1959, '60, '62, '65, '70 and '72. In 1971 he received a $15,000 Molson Prize from the Canada Council, an honour presented for "a man's total career rather than any single work." In 1976 Macpherson was elected to the Canadian News Hall of Fame.

Phil Mallette was born in Sault Ste. Marie in 1955 but considers himself a native of Kirkland Lake, Ontario, where he grew up. After graduating from the University of Guelph in 1977 with a Bachelor of Arts degree in Fine Arts, he began working as a freelance cartoonist and illustrator in Toronto. When *Globe and Mail* cartoonist Tony Jenkins took an extended leave of absence in 1981 to travel, Phil sat in for him doing cartoons for the *Globe's* editorial page on Ed Franklin's days off as well as doing spot illustrations. Phil Mallette's cartoons appear regularly in *The Saturday Winnipeg Free Press* and *The Financial Post*. His work as illustrator has appeared in *The Financial Post Magazine, Canadian Business Magazine, Toronto Life, The Globe & Mail* and various other publications.

Malcolm Mayes was born in Edmonton, Alberta in 1962. After puberty and some encouragement from cartoonist Yardley Jones, he began to push a pencil on a regular basis. While studying Art at Grant Mac Ewan College, he started a company, Mayes Feature Service, to distribute his cartoons to publications across Alberta. He sold drawings to *The Calgary Herald, The Lethbridge Herald, Western Report* and *The Red Deer Advocate,* before starting as the editorial-page cartoonist for *The Edmonton Journal* in June of this year.

A Toronto commercial artist who's been with the Union Art Service since June '84, **Ken Munro** would much rather be on the P.G.A. Tour but hasn't a hope in hell. Studied graphic design at George Brown College, Toronto. After extensive travelling through the Far East (past Halifax) with 1½-year pit-stop as an English teacher in Japan, he still has trouble with the fact that even though he cartoons for the labour movement he doesn't make as much money as them... but at least he's got a job.

Dan Murphy does cartoons for *The Province* in Vancouver, Canada Wide, and Rothco.

Len Norris was born in London, England in 1913 and moved with his family to Port Arthur, Ontario. He later moved to Toronto where he took night courses at The Ontario College of Art for one year. He worked as an art director for an ad agency from 1938 to 1940, when he joined the Army. For five years after the war he worked as an art director for Maclean-Hunter, working on various magazines, before heading out to Vancouver, where he had been offered a job at *The Vancouver Sun*. Norris won the National Newspaper Award the first year he entered, in 1951 and the *Sun* produced annual collections of Norris' cartoons for twenty-seven years. Eventually Norris became as much a symbol of BC as the totem pole. In 1973 the University of Windsor granted Norris an Honorary Doctorate of Law. Norris retired in 1978, but continues to draw two cartoons a week for the *Sun*. He has been elected to both the Canadian News Hall Fame and the Royal Canadian Academy of Arts.

"Oh, oh... we've run out of tax."

Born in Winnipeg in 1936, **Roy Peterson** works for *The Vancouver Sun* and *Maclean's* magazine and does occasional op. ed. page work for *The Toronto Star*. His work has appeared in all major Canadian and most major American newspapers and magazines as well as *Punch* and *The Spectator* in Britain. He has worked on newspapers, magazines and books as a team with Allan Fotheringham and with Stanley Burke on the bestselling *Frog Fables & Beaver Tales* series. Has illustrated many book covers and produced his own children's book *The Canadian ABC Book* as well as a collection of his cartoons *The World According to Roy Peterson* and *Drawn & Quartered*, a collection of editorial cartoons pertaining to the Trudeau years with text by Peter C. Newman. Married, with five children, he was, in 1982-83, the first Canadian-born president of the Association of American Editorial Cartoonists. He won the grand prize at the International Salon of Cartoons in Montréal in 1973 and is three-time winner of the National Newspaper Award.

Roland Pier was born in France in 1936. He came to Canada in 1960, travelled extensively, and had various jobs including construction and working at a gold mine. Arriving in Montréal in 1962, he began freelancing and was eventually hired by *Le Journal de Montréal* as a political cartoonist. *Le Journal* has since become the largest French-language newspaper in North America. As Pier's cartoons also appear in a sister publication, *Le Journal de Québec,* he is undoubtedly the most widely read cartoonist in Québec today.

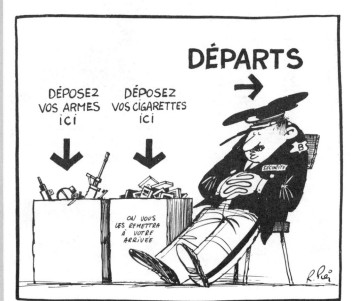

Born in 1935 in Hamilton, Ontario, **Denny Pritchard** worked in auto plants in Ontario. He began as free-lancer in 1975 and is now employed as staff cartoonist by the Saskatoon *Star Phoenix*.

Born July 1st, 1957, in Dunedin, New Zealand, **Adrian Raeside** got his start in cartooning, drawing on the back of bus seats on his way home from school. Moving to Canada in 1972, after a brief period in England, he worked at various jobs, from land surveying on the Northern BC coast, to unloading grain cars in a Thunder Bay grain elevator, before realizing he wasn't much good at any of them. Getting his first break in 1976, illustrating five children's books his mother Joan had written, he quickly became one of the most popular cartoonists on Wildwood Crescent. Living on Saltspring Island, he commutes to the Victoria *Times Colonist,* where he has been the editorial cartoonist for the past six years. As well as being widely syndicated in Canada, through his own syndicate, his work also appears in a number of U.S. publications. He has never won an award, and is not president of anything.

Born in Edmonton in 1946, **Vance Rodewalt** worked at *The Roughnecks,* after completing high school, where he did advertising cartoons. After working for Marvel Comics for 5 years, he travelled to Europe and, upon his return, began doing political cartoons for the Calgary *Albertan*. When the *Albertan* was bought by *The Calgary Sun,* he remained there for 3½ years before moving on to *The Calgary Herald* were he has been sharing editorial page cartooning duties with Tom Innes since the spring of 1983.

Born in 1955 in Montreal, **David Rosen** is a freelance cartoonist and sometime writer. In 1984 he published *Megatoons: Cartoonists Against Nuclear War* and is currently working on a book about Canada's radical cartoonists. He is also Canadian editor of *Target,* a quarterly devoted to the art of political cartooning.

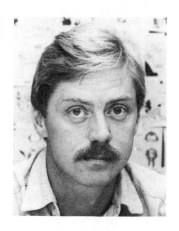

Ting is the pen-name of **Merle Tingley,** political cartoonist for *The London Free Press.* Born and raised in Montréal, he studied art for one year and then worked briefly as a draughtsman until joining the army at the beginning of the Second World War. He began drawing cartoons on a full-time basis for the *Free Press* in 1948 and received the National Newspaper Award in 1955. He has now retired but still does two drawings a week on a freelance basis.

Jim Todd works as a self-syndicated freelance cartoonist for various newspapers in Atlantic Canada. He is a native of and presently resides in the small community of Perotte in southwestern Nova Scotia, and like most freelancers, is eventually hoping to work as a full-time editorial cartoonist for a daily paper. His cartoons have been published in a variety of Canadian and American political cartoon collections, as well as other piublications and textbooks in the Maritimes and Ontario. His illustrations appear regularly in *Policy Options* magazine, published by the Institute for Research on Public Policy.

Since his debut at *The Edmonton Journal* in 1968, **Edd Uluschak**'s acclaim and popularity have been indisputable. Twice the recipient of both the National Newspaper Award for Cartooning and the Basil Dean Memorial Award for Journalistic Merit, Edd has also won many international awards and prizes. Edd, his wife Susan their two children and his pet racoon now make their home on five-acres of paradise on Gabriola Island, BC.

Born in London, England in 1926, **Ben Wicks** claims to have held the Nazi hordes at bay during the war as a swimming pool attendant at a Canterbury army camp. Having learned to play the saxophone in the army, he toured Europe with a band and was later to play in the orchestra on the liner Queen Elizabeth. Wicks moved to Canada in 1957, working as a milkman in Calgary. He sold several gag cartoons to *The Saturday Evening Post* and has never looked back. Moving to Toronto in 1960, he produces a daily syndicated cartoon (*Wicks*) in addition to his daily comic strip, *The Outcasts*. Organiser of last year's Thanksgiving African hunger relief effort, he was, this year, named to the Order of Canada.

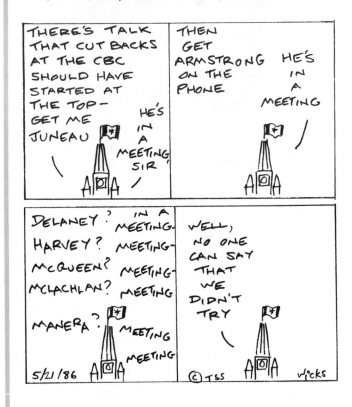

"It's Statistics Canada... demanding that you, Joseph Marmaduke Bloggs, of 2194 West 169th Street, born March 12, 1937, Rockbottom Creek, B.C., parents Marmaduke and Marcelle Boggs, married to Penelope nee Muggs June 1, 1956, three children age 31, 21, and 2, show cause for not filling in census form on penalty of..."